Printed and published in Great Britain by D.C. Thomson & Co., Ltd.,
185 Fleet Street, London.
© **D.C. THOMSON & CO., LTD., 1994.**
(Certain stories do not appear exactly as originally published.)
ISBN O 85116 590-7

DANDY and BEANO

FIFTY YEARS OF FUN

DENNIS,
DAN AND
FRIENDS
TELL THEIR
OWN STORIES

A FEW WORDS FROM . . .
DENNIS the MENACE

Just thought I'd introduce myself in case any of you have spent the last 43 years up the Amazon without a paddle, or on a desert island with no newsagents! Everyone else will **KNOW** I'm Britain's biggest menace! And everyone (that means **YOU!!!**) will love my menacing selection from **BEANO'S** back pages!

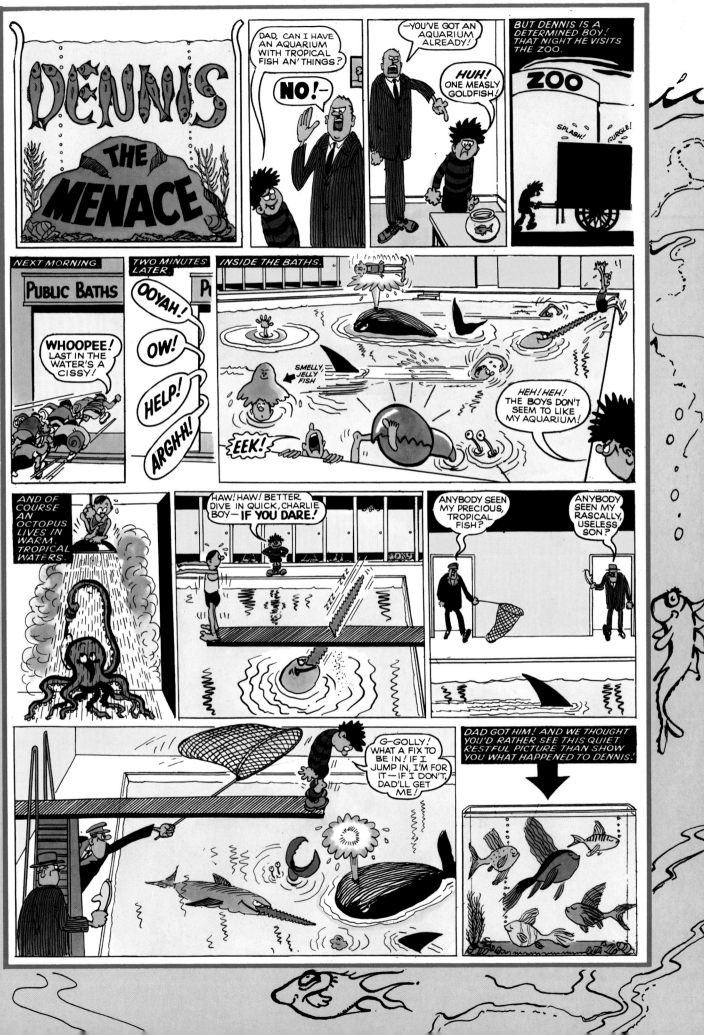

In the early 1960s the great British public (or The Dennis The Menace Fan Club, as I call it) had the chance to enjoy even more menacing stories when The **BEANO** Summer Special was launched. As you can see, menaces don't take holidays — it's an all year round occupation!

GOLF MENACE

Grab an eyeful (or golf-bag full) of these goodies. My golfing fans can now have their very own Dennis The Menace golf balls, tees, ball markers, pitch-mark repairers, club head covers, golf towels, polo shirts, caps and visors . . . All items are from the Official Dennis The Menace Gift Catalogue launched early 1994. You'd go a fair way to find a better collection.

GOLFING MENACES AND

MENACING GOLFERS

DENNIS THE MENACE . . .

I've broken a few records in my time, plus one or two windows, a couple of vases and a few other bits and pieces. (LOTS of pieces by the time I'm finished). Here are some of my memorable moments.

THE GRINNERS BOOK OF RECORDS

SHARP SHOOTING CHAMPION

The shooting comes first followed by a sharp exit.

DRIVING CHAMP

No one bumps more cars on the dodgems than me. I'm the Champ at driving Dad bananas.

POLICE RECORD

Don't panic, fans! I haven't turned to a life of crime. Our local P.C. was unlucky enough to be around during me and my pals' record-breaking attempts on the opposite page.

BERYL THE PERIL . . .

... TELLS HER OWN STORY

BERYL THE PERIL . . .

What have I in common with Dennis The Menace and Desperate Dan? Be careful how you answer . . . I'm much prettier than either of those guys. Come to think of it I've seen better looking wart-hogs, but don't tell 'em I said that. I want to stay pretty . . . The answer is I've starred in my very own books just like Dennis and Dan. The first one went on sale in time for Christmas 1958. Here are just a few of the great-looking covers.

KORKY THE CAT TELLS HIS OWN STORY

I reckon that anyone who's starred in a best-selling comic for more than 50 years deserves letters after their name, so I've awarded myself a few. Now meet Korky The Cat K.O.F. — that stands for Keen On Fish and if you're wondering just how much I like fish, read on . . .

Forget about fish and chips — I like fish and Christmas.

You've read my fishy tales — now join me for a cool Yule!

LORD SNOOTY TELLS HIS OWN STORY

Aunt Mat is in charge of my pocket money, and when it comes to being tight-fisted she could give Ebenezer Scrooge lessons. That's why I'm just as broke as the rest of my gang in the story below . . .

LORD SNOOTY TELLS HIS OWN STORY

The **BEANO'S** titled toff behind bars! The comic world's premier peer in prison! How could such a thing happen? For the full story, read on . . .

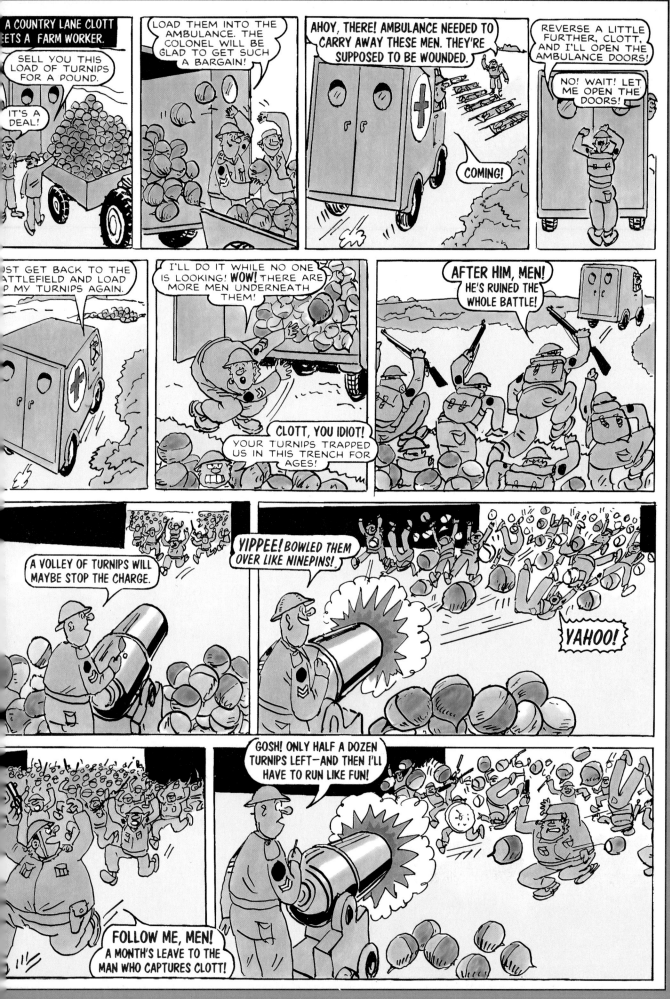

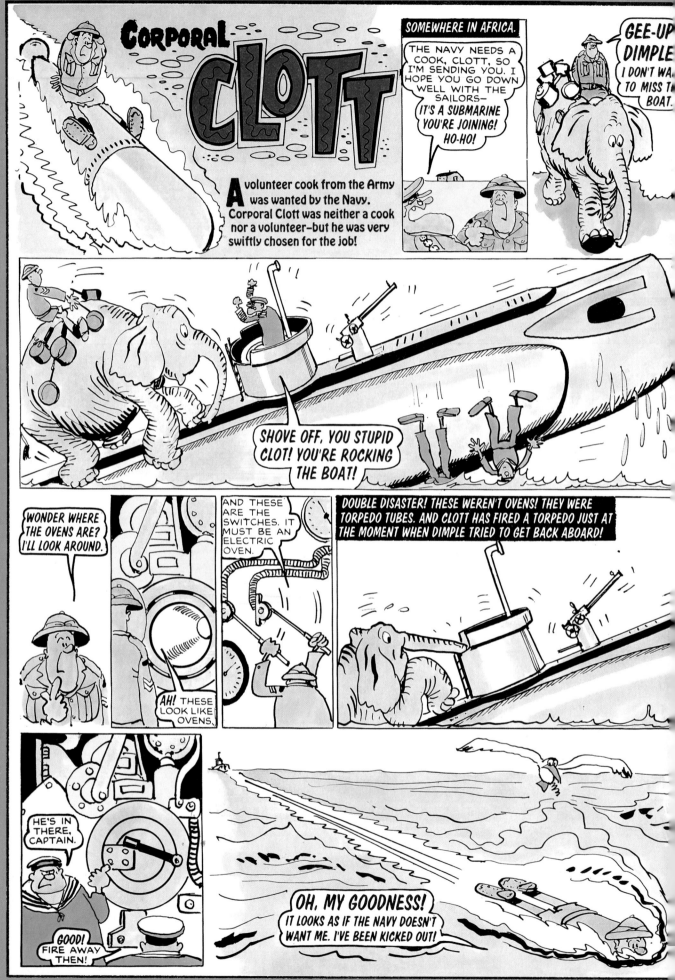

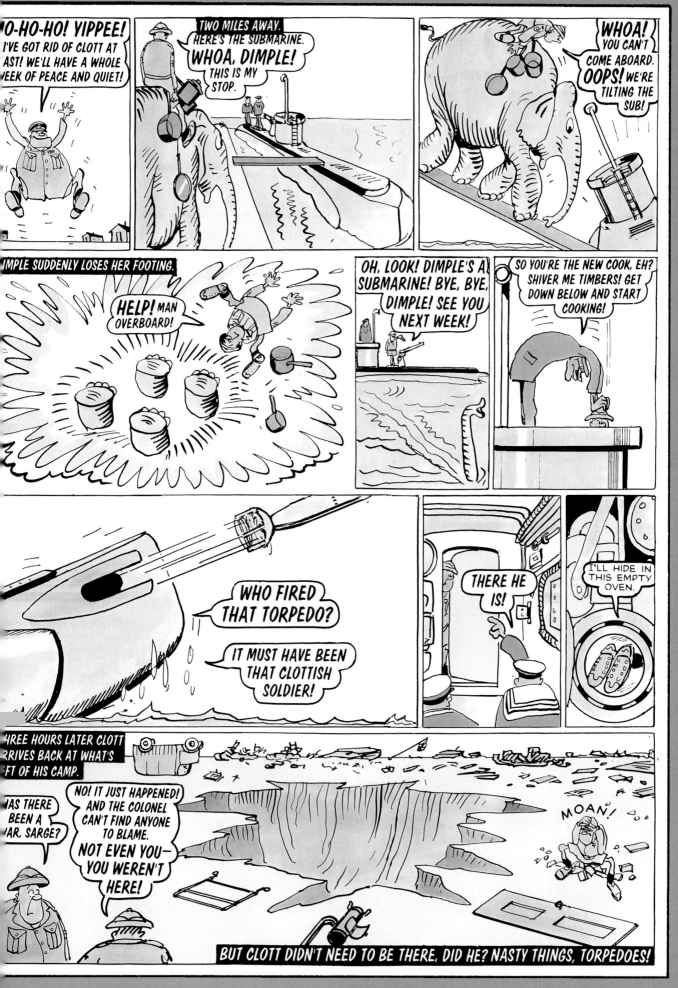

PRIZE-GIVING

SPORTS DAY

THE BASH STREET KIDS

A REPORT BY TEACHER

Class II B of Bash Street School are the worst pupils I've ever taught. Come to think of it, they're the only pupils I've ever taught. I wasted my time studying to be a teacher when I should have been training with the S.A.S. On second thoughts, even the S.A.S. wouldn't stand a chance against the Bash Street Kids.

I have recently discovered that the prison on Devil's Island is now vacant and I believe it would make an ideal 'school' for the little horrors. I would, of course, not be joining them.

This report must not fall into the grubby little hands of Class II B.

SHREDDER IIIII

SCHOOL CONCERT

CLASS II B

THE BASH STREET KIDS . . .

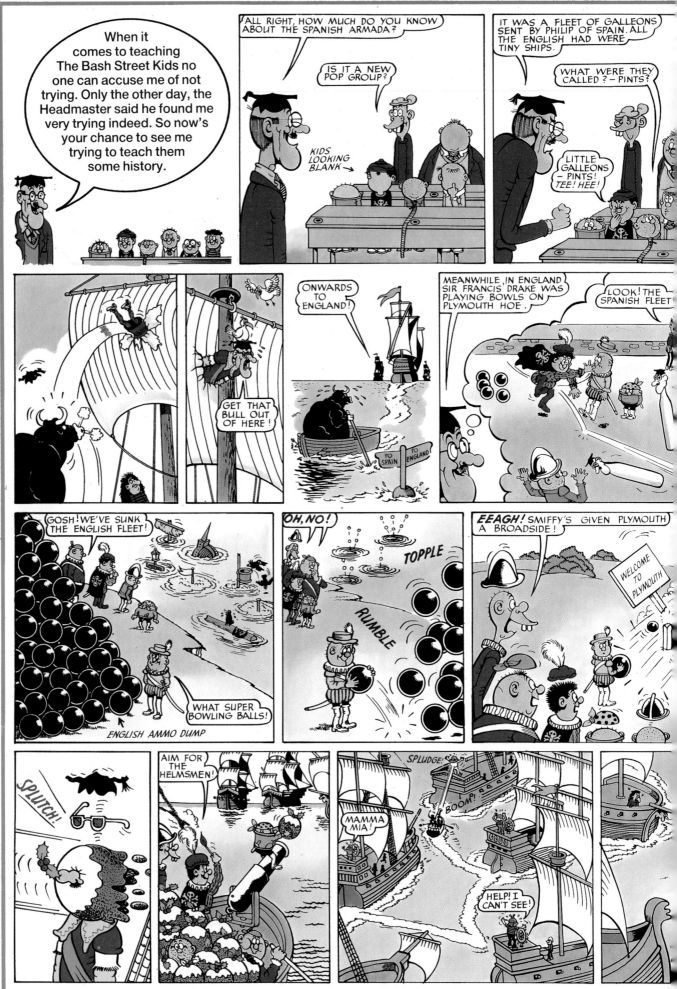

Don't get the wrong idea and think Teacher often comes off best. After the school trip he definitely didn't want to be beside the seaside . . . thanks to US!

YOU ARE TO TAKE THE CHILDREN ON A NATURE RAMBLE TO THE SEASIDE. THERE'S TO BE NO PADDLING, NO DIGGING IN THE SAND, NO ROCK-CLIMBING AND NO DIVING. UNDERSTAND?
HEAD'S STUDY
FISH NET
YESSIR!
NOW REMEMBER! YOU HAVE TO BEHAVE WHILE WE'RE AT THE SEASIDE.
BOO! WE WANT TO PADDLE AN' SWIM AN' DIVE AN' DIG AN' CLIMB!
ROTTEN TEACHER
SCHOOL BUS
GRR! I SAID 'NO PADDLING!' HERBERT HAND ME MY CANE!
RUBBER GLOVE
TUT-TUT! I THOUGHT YOU SAID 'NO PADDLING.'
AARGH! IT'S AN ELECTRIC EEL!
SIZZ
SPLOSH!
GASHP! CHOKE! GURGLE! AGHSH! MY FALSH TEEF!
QUICK SANDS
BLOOP!
LEND ME YOUR SHPADE, SHONNY!
TUT-TUT, TEACHER! NO DIGGING ALLOWED!
SQUAWK! THIS'LL MAKE A SMASHIN' NEST!
QUICK SANDS
TUT-TUT, TEACHER! NO ROCK-CLIMBING!
I MUST GET MY MORTAR-BOARD BACK!
PECK! PECK!
PECKED!
TUT-TUT, TEACHER! NO DIVING!
EEEAGH!
PYONNG!
PYONNG!
SPLOSH!
MEANWHILE— BACK ON THE PROMENADE.
GRR! I'VE JUST WATCHED NAUGHTY TEACHER DOING ALL THE THINGS I FORBADE THE CLASS TO DO!—
PENNY A PEEP!
— I SHALL SEND HIM BACK TO SCHOOL IN DISGRACE!
YIPPEE!
ROLLER COASTER
TO THE RAILWAY STATION
THEN THE HEAD TAKES THE KIDS ON A SPREE— SO THEY WON'T BE DISAPPOINTED ABOUT MISSING THE NATURE RAMBLE!

August 4, 1962 — a great day for Bash Street fans — our first two-page story in The BEANO weekly.

Someone once asked me if The Bash Street Kids like a joke . . . Is Dennis a menace?!? Is Roger a dodger?!? We don't just like jokes . . . we LOVE 'em! And, believe it or not, the biggest joke we ever played wasn't on Teacher, it was on YOU our loyal readers.

February, 1994, our 40th birthday, and to celebrate this great event a three-week story appeared in The BEANO. But strange things were happening. The old Bash Street School building was condemned and replaced with a shiny modern one. Teacher, Headmaster and the rest of the staff were sacked and their jobs given to robots. In fact everything changed — Plug even became handsome!

And did this new look go down well with our millions of adoring fans? NO! NO! NO! Before the third, and final, part of the story reached the newsagents, The BEANO editor was swamped with protests. Readers were even sad to see the back of Teacher (Personally, I love to see the back of Teacher — it's great for target practice!) But you'd all jumped the gun! By the end of the story we were back to normal (and Plug was back to abnormal). We'd returned to our old school, and just to prove that nothing in life is ever quite perfect — Teacher was 'in charge' again!

But best of all, it proved that Bash Street fans can take a joke!

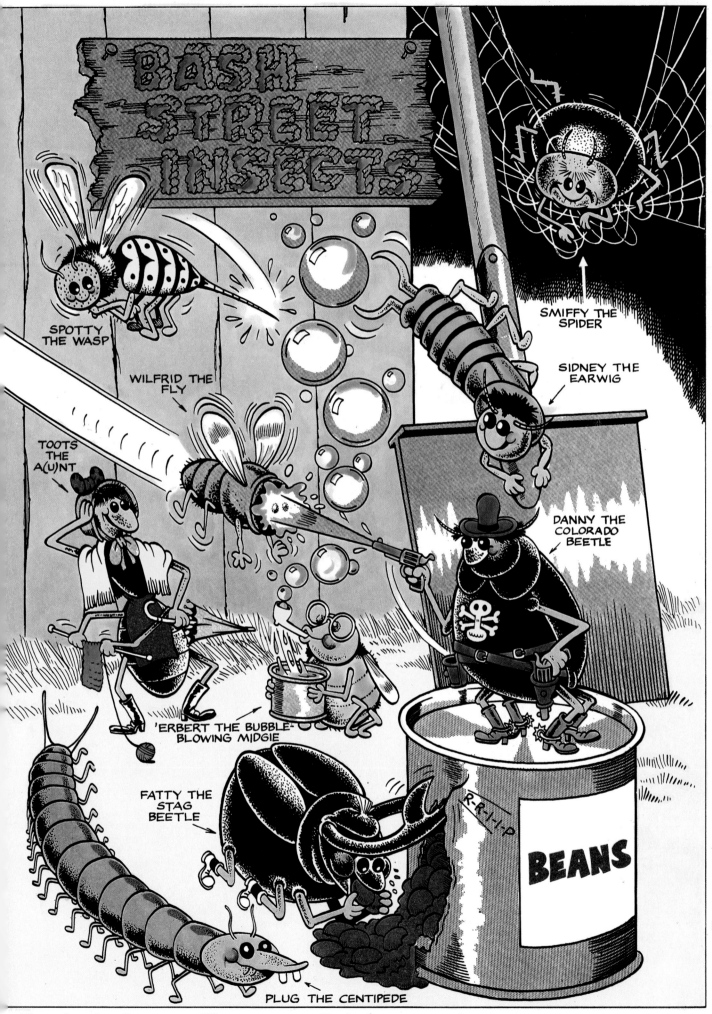

Teacher's always calling us nasty little beasts and even he has to be right occasionally. To prove it, earwigo with a feature from the 1971 BEANO book.

FORGET THE TERMINATOR AND THE EQUALIZER! MEET . . .

The Collector!

Gary Blurton thinks big! He's almost certainly the owner of the world's largest collection of anything and everything connected with DANDY and BEANO. When other comic fans buy a Dennis mug or a Desperate Dan sweatshirt Gary purchases a pile of 'em! And if you need proof, take a look at these photographs of the house Gary shares with his family in Uttoxeter.

Gary began collecting comics, then decided to decorate his room with Dennis wallpaper. After that it was buy, buy, buy . . . and 'bye-'bye to around £20,000 of Gary's hard-earned cash, money made from his two jobs with a builders' merchant and a newsagent's shop.

While other folk are putting out the cat last thing at night, Gary is busy scooping up piles of DANDY and BEANO goodies that are stored on his bed, so he can slip under his Dennis duvet for a good night's sleep.

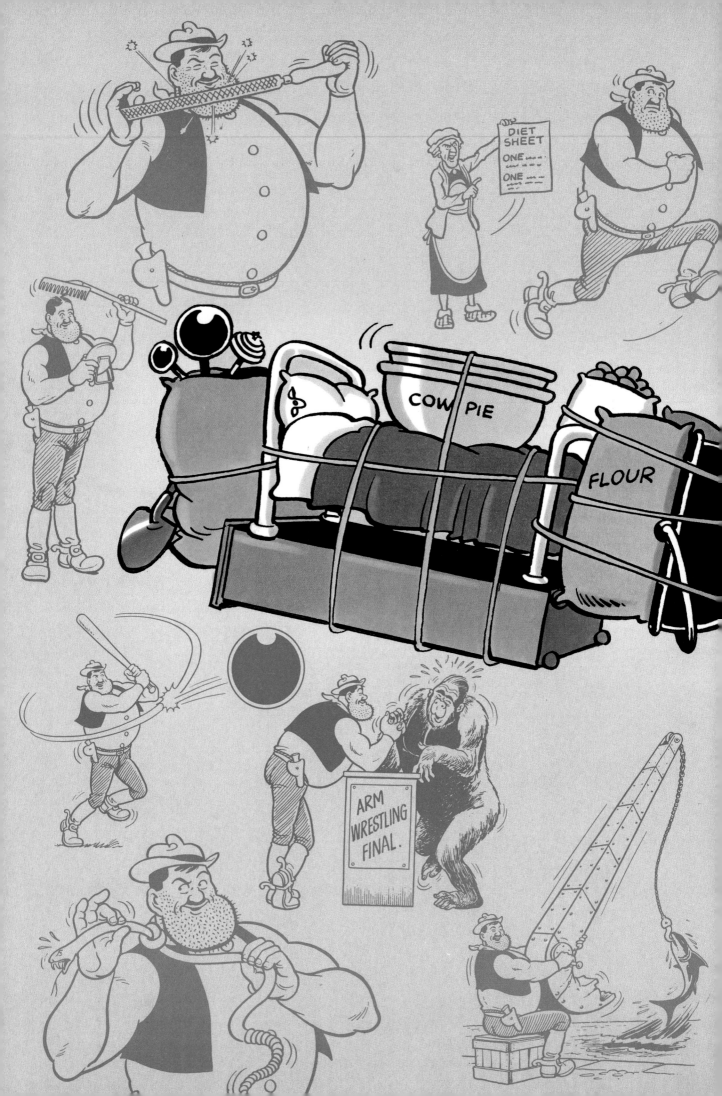

DESPERATE DAN

here, the Texas tough guy who's spent the last 57 (count 'em if you don't believe me!) years grappling with grizzlies, wallopin' wildcats, wrestlin' rattlesnakes and helpin' little ol' ladies across the street. An' I've gotta admit it gets scarey at times. Yup! Helpin' mah Aunt Aggie to cross the road ain't for the faint-hearted. She can be a mighty stern woman. But enough of this big guy's small-talk. If you want Desperate Dan stories, you've come to the right place. I've chosen a bundle so stand by for a Dan-sized helpin' of fun! A dandy time is guaranteed.

THE GRINNERS BOOK OF RECORDS

When I played football with a stone ball I flattened a record number of trees. The lumberjack said, "You've done the work of tree fellers, Dan!" I told him I'd done the work of at least FOUR fellahs!

I reckon getting 18 birdies is some kinda record, especially if you ain't playin' golf!

I must be the world champion wind surfer. All the other guys are real softies. They use boards.

My record-breakin' attempts at putting-the-shott have brought the house down, but this was the first time I had that effect on a tent.

No one sneezes harder than me! Last time I sneezed I raised the roof — quite a few of 'em in fact! Here are some of my record-breaking . . .

A-A-A-A-CHIEVEMENTS!!!

ON YER BIKE! . . . Yup!
You can't beat the feel
of a set of wheels — in
mah case — STEEL
wheels! Here's a few of
the bikes 'n' trikes I've
ridden over the years!

BUTCHER

GROCER

FISH

I even
earned some
cash on mah bike,
when I worked as
Cactusville's biggest
telegram boy!

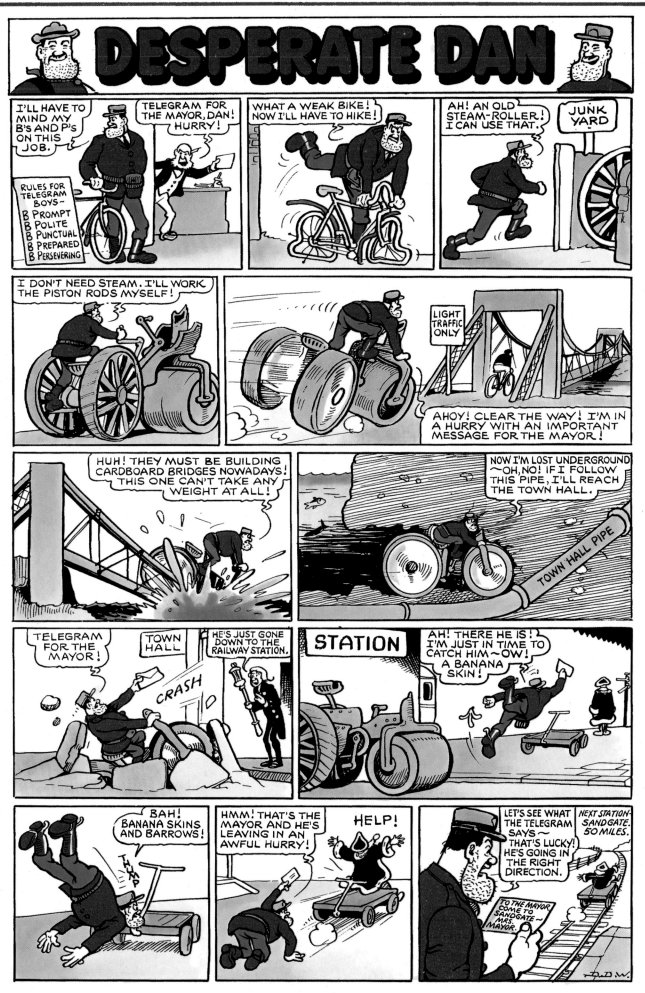

Buster might be my best buddy but that doesn't mean I don't play a trick on him now and again . . . I mean what are friends for?

JONAH . . .

Have I always been a dodger? The short answer's 'YES!' and the short dodger
on the following pages is a very young me!

BANANAMAN . . .

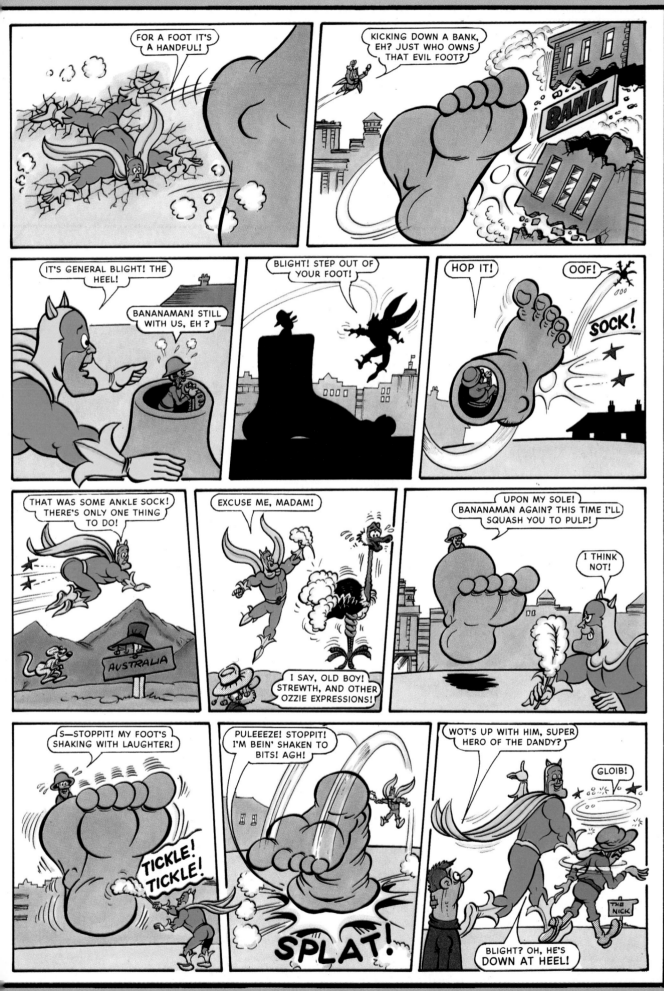

THE DIARY OF MINNIE THE MINX

MINDAY — The day I introduce myself and my family to the readers with the MINNIEmum of fuss. They'll meet my parents and discover that Dad was once voted the world's unluckiest man. (Can't imagine why!) I won't reveal my age. I'll just say I'm younger than Roger The Dodger but older than The Bash Street Kids. And most important of all, I must put my diaries in a nice safe place!

ZAP!

NEWS at TEN

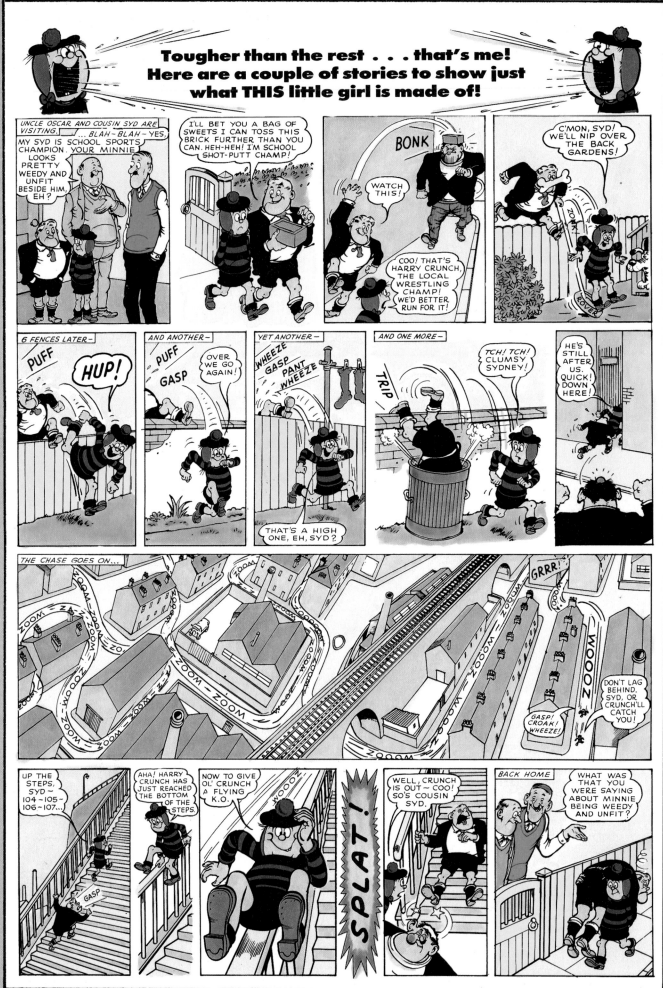

WINKER WATSON...

that's me! And that pile back there is Greytowers School, home to yours truly since 1961. They call me the wily wangler because of my schemes and tricks, and if you're wondering why they call my teacher Mr Creep, just turn the page...

LITTLE PLUM

MESSAGE PAD

PLEASE KNOCK

SMOKE GETS IN YOUR EYES

Here's the translation of my smoke signals for the less well-educated readers who don't understand smoke language.

Little Plum's the name . . . puff . . . my dad worked on the railroad as an Injun engine driver . . . puff . . . and sometimes Mum would help him . . puff . . . she was an Injun engineer . . . puff . . . I've been a BEANO star since 1953 . . . puff . . . and I've had a grizzly time with the peskiest pests in the west — GRIZZLY BEARS . . . puff . . . and here are three stories to prove it . . . Have to stop now, I'm running out of puff!

If you thought those beasts were badly
behaved, you ain't seen nothin' yet. Turn the page for
an extra-big helping of battling bears.

RETURN of the MENACE

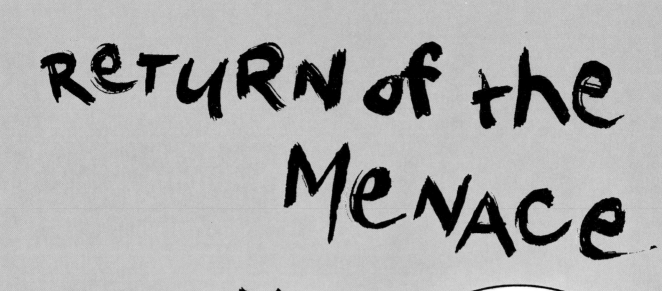

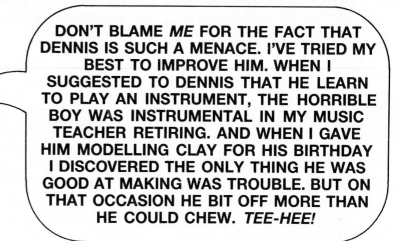

DON'T BLAME *ME* FOR THE FACT THAT DENNIS IS SUCH A MENACE. I'VE TRIED MY BEST TO IMPROVE HIM. WHEN I SUGGESTED TO DENNIS THAT HE LEARN TO PLAY AN INSTRUMENT, THE HORRIBLE BOY WAS INSTRUMENTAL IN MY MUSIC TEACHER RETIRING. AND WHEN I GAVE HIM MODELLING CLAY FOR HIS BIRTHDAY I DISCOVERED THE ONLY THING HE WAS GOOD AT MAKING WAS TROUBLE. BUT ON THAT OCCASION HE BIT OFF MORE THAN HE COULD CHEW. *TEE-HEE!*

PYONG!

MIAOW! SCREECH!

DENNIS!

TWANG!

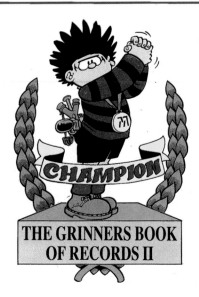

CHAMPION
THE GRINNERS BOOK OF RECORDS II

HIGH JUMP CHAMP
Dad's often told me, "You're for the high jump, my lad!" and this time he was right. Watch me go up in the world — breaking the high jump and high chomp records with a single leap.

YOU'LL BE BOWLED OVER and googly-eyed too when you see my high-speed, long-distance, under-hand, over-arm, super-powered bowling.

If there's one thing I like breaking more than records, it's rules — and I break a few of both in the story below.

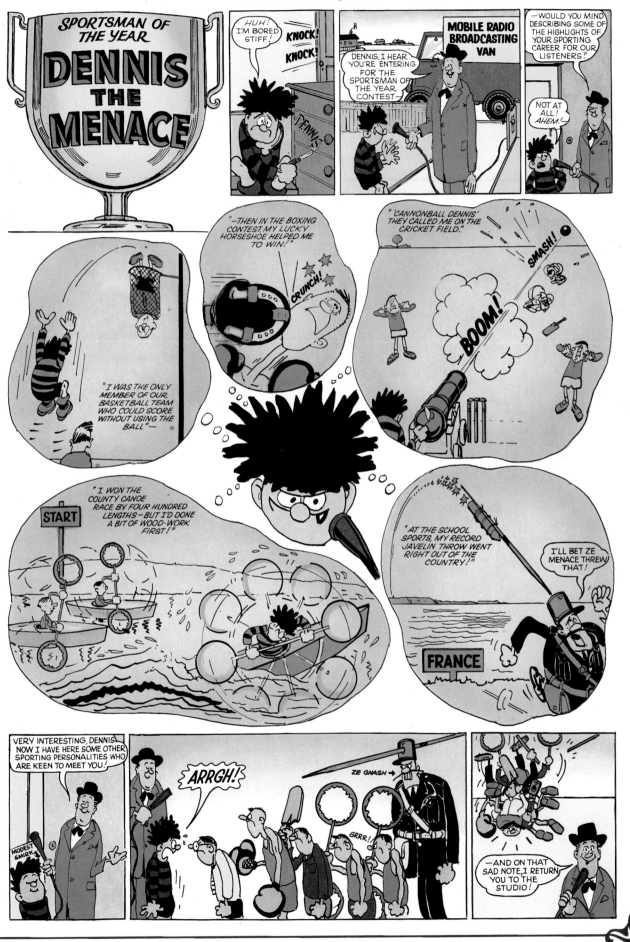